FROGS ARE FUNNY!

THIS **MOST** SENSATIONAL, INSPIRATIONAL, CELEBRATIONAL, **MUPPETATIONAL** MUPPETS JOKE BOOK EVER!

BY
The Muppets

WITH
Brandon T. Snider

PaRragon

Bath · New York · Singapore · Hong Kong · Cologne · Delhi
Melbourne · Amsterdam · Johannesburg · Auckland · Shenzhen

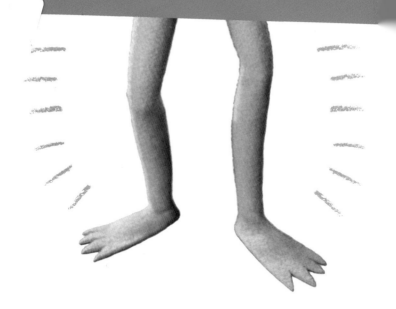

AS A TADPOLE,
I ALWAYS WANTED TO BE A DANCER

BUT YOU KNOW WHAT THEY SAY

THE FIRST THINGS TO GO
ON A FROG

ARE HIS LEGS! ☺

I like the movie so far.

IT HASN'T STARTED YET.

That's why I like it! ☺

I'M SO NERVOUS!

IF I'M NOT **FUNNY** I WON'T KNOW HOW TO LIVE WITH MYSELF.

THEN YOU'LL HAVE TO GET A
NEW APARTMENT,
WON'T YOU? ☺

HA HA
HA HA HA
HA HA

HOW WOULD YOU LIKE A PORK CHOP?

HIII-YAH!

YOU ALWAYS HURT THE ONE YOU **LOVE.** ☺

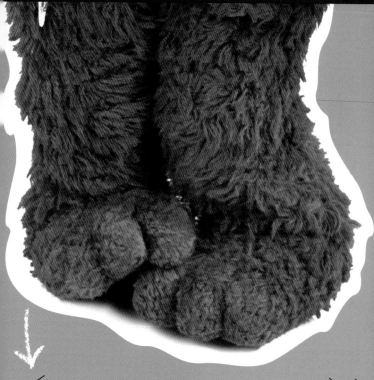

I HAVE A DRESSING ROOM SO SMALL...

ALL THE MICE ARE HUNCHBACKS! ☺

I'D LOVE TO BE ON BROADWAY.

Yeah, I can see your name in lights: **25 watts!**

25 WATTS?
THAT'S NOT VERY BRIGHT.

Look who's talking!

DR STRANGEPORK,
WHY ARE WE PLUMMETING TO
EARTH AT AN ALARMING RATE?

WE'VE LOST THE
NUMBER THREE
ENGINE!

WELL, HOW LONG WILL IT TAKE TO FIX IT?

WE CAN'T!

IT'S REALLY LOST!

IT FELL OFF!

13

I JUST WANT TO KNOW MORE ABOUT THIS WEDDING SKETCH. I MEAN, I'VE GOT TO **learn my lines, Piggy.**

WELL, YOU ONLY HAVE ONE LINE.

I do? ???

EXACTLY! ☺

I HOPE YOU APPRECIATE THAT I'M DOING ALL

MY OWN STUNTS. ☺

YOU SHOULD NEVER
EAT THE COMEDIAN!

THEY TASTE

FUNNY!

HA
HA
HA
HAAAAAAA! ☺

HA HA HA HA HA HA HA HA HA

WHAT KIND OF DOCTOR DO YOU THINK I AM?

QUACK!

I SHOULD KNOW BETTER
THAN TO ASK A

CHICKEN. ☺

DR BOB, CHICKENS DO NOT QUACK.

THEY DO WHEN THEY'RE YOUNG.

THEY DO?

Sure. If you drop
an egg, it'll

QUACK! ☺

21

A GUY WALKS INTO A DINER.

THERE'S A HORSE BEHIND
THE COUNTER. THE HORSE JUST
LOOKS AT THE GUY AND SAYS,

"What's the matter?
Surprised to see me here?"

AND THE GUY SAYS,

" Yeah, did the cow
sell the place?" ☺

THIS APPLE HAS A WORM IN IT.

THAT'S NOT A WORM—
IT'S MY TAIL! ☺

Say the bear was **magnificent!** After all, I did the driving!

AND I TOOK A HUNDRED-FOOT BELLY FLOP ONTO A MOVING CAR!

(CONT.)

YES, BUT KERMIT ASSUMED THE AWESOME RESPONSIBILITY OF

COMMAND!

GEE.

THIRD-RATE ENTERTAINMENT!☺

YOU'RE SUCH A SMOOTH DANCER.
EVER SINCE WE'VE STARTED, I FEEL LIKE
MY FEET HAVE NEVER TOUCHED THE FLOOR.

They haven't.
You've been standing on mine. ☺

WE'VE GOT A BIG MUSICAL FINALE
FROM SAM THE EAGLE,
SAM, TELL US: WHAT'S IT ABOUT?

IT'S CALLED
'A SALUTE TO ALL NATIONS.

**But Mostly
America.'** ☺

I GO OUT WITH A LOVELY GIRL.

She's so bow-legged,

WHEN SHE STANDS
AROUND THE HOUSE,

SHE STANDS

AROUND THE HOUSE! ☺

I STAYED
AT A HOTEL

so exclusive

THAT ROOM SERVICE WAS

AN UNLISTED NUMBER! ☺

HERE'S YOUR NEXT PATIENT.

Hey, this is just a shoe!

WHAT HAPPENED TO THE REST OF HIM?

Maybe he got cold feet! ☺

IRRI-TATED!
IRRI-TATED!

DON'T WORRY,
ANIMAL,
YOUR BIG SCENE
IS COMING UP.

YEAH, JUST BE COOL
AND EAT ANOTHER
SEAT CUSHION.

SEEEAT
CUSH-ION! ☺

I throw fish into the air, and then they sail away and come back to me!

I DON'T CARE ABOUT

BOOMERANG
FISH ACTS!

(CONT.)

YOU WILL . . .

THEY'RE COMING BACK! ☺

AHEM. I WOULD JUST LIKE TO SAY A FEW WORDS ABOUT **NUDITY** IN THE WORLD TODAY. I, FOR ONE, AM JUST APPALLED BY IT.

WHY, DID YOU KNOW THAT UNDERNEATH THEIR CLOTHING, THE ENTIRE POPULATION OF THE WORLD IS WALKING AROUND COMPLETELY **NAKED?** HMM?

ISN'T THAT DISGUSTING?

AND IT'S NOT JUST PEOPLE, ALTHOUGH, GOODNESS KNOWS, THAT'S BAD ENOUGH. EVEN CUTE LITTLE DOGGIES AND PUSSYCATS CAN'T BE TRUSTED. UNDERNEATH THEIR FUR, AB-SO-LUTE-LY **NAKED!** AND IT'S NOT JUST THE QUADRUPEDS, EITHER. BIRDS, TOO! YES! BENEATH THOSE FINE FEATHERS, BIRDS WEAR

NOTHING! NOTHING AT ALL!

ABSO-... ☺

THESE TWO CANNIBALS WERE TALKING.
ONE CANNIBAL SAYS TO THE OTHER CANNIBAL,

"WHO WAS THAT LADY
I SAW YOU WITH
LAST NIGHT?"

THE OTHER CANNIBAL SAYS,

"THAT WAS NO LADY- THAT WAS MY LUNCH!" ☺

I SUGGEST WE
JUMP.

Are you crazy?

THAT'S AT LEAST A
HUNDRED FEET!

I DIDN'T SAY
IT WAS A GOOD
SUGGESTION. ☻

MAKE READY FOR THE CAPTAIN! DAWDLERS WILL SUFFER HIS WRATH!

Is the captain bad tempered?

THE MAN IS A RAGING VOLCANO, TORMENTED BY INNER DEMONS THE LIKES OF WHICH MERE MORTALS CANNOT FATHOM.

He's got demons?
Cool! ☺

MY HOUSE IS SO DIRTY...

MY DOG BURIES HIS BONES
IN THE LIVING ROOM CARPET.

WE GOT OUR **MONEY'S** WORTH TONIGHT!

BUT WE PAID NOTHING.

THAT'S WHAT WE GOT! ☺

SMELL THAT AIR!
OH MY GOSH!
HOW THE WORLD HAS CHANGED!

WHAT EVER HAPPENED
TO THE TRAM?
AND MEN
WITH HATS?

WE WERE IN JAIL FOR FOUR HOURS, GONZO.

GEE, IT FELT LIKE FORTY YEARS! ☺

THIS IS GREAT, GONZO—
YOU POPPED THE FLASH
JUST BEFORE THE SOUP
LANDED ON HIS TIE.

YEAH, WELL, PHOTOGRAPHY IS AN ART. YOU'VE GOT TO HAVE THE RIGHT FILM, THE RIGHT EXPOSURE... AND YOU'VE GOT TO **SCREAM** JUST BEFORE THEY GET THE FOOD IN THEIR MOUTH. ☺

WE'RE GONNA CATCH THOSE THIEVES RED-HANDED.

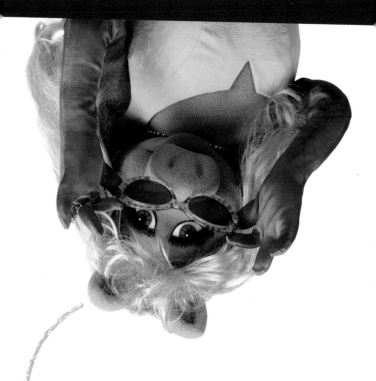

WHAT COLOUR ARE THEIR HANDS NOW? ☺

IN OUR HOUSE
WE USE PAPER PLATES.

Every night after dinner my wife

ERASES

the dishes. ☺

THIS SHOW IS GOOD FOR WHAT AILS ME.

WHAT AILS YOU?

INSOMNIA. ☺

DR BUNSEN HONEYDEW HERE, AT THE MUPPET LABS, WHERE THE FUTURE IS BEING MADE TODAY.

NOW, THE HONOUR OF TASTING THIS FIRST BATCH OF DELICIOUS PAPER CLIPS GOES OF COURSE TO MY HELPFUL AND EAGER ASSISTANT,

BEAKER.

NUH UH!

NOW, BEAKER, WHAT IS THE MATTER?

MEE MEE MEE! ☺

YES, FRIENDS, MUPPETS' EDIBLE PAPER CLIPS ARE DELICIOUS, NUTRITIOUS, AND NICKEL-PLATED. THEY'RE HANDY AROUND THE OFFICE, AND THEY ARE WONDERFUL AS A TV SNACK! FURTHERMORE, THEY ARE ABSOLUTELY HARMLESS-

. . . OR NEARLY SO. ☺

The poor fellow lost his nose!

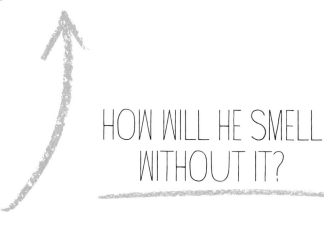

HOW WILL HE SMELL WITHOUT IT?

Same as always- TERRIBLE! ☺

MY DEAR,
YOU ARE SO **BEAUTIFUL.**

HAVE I SEEN YOU
IN THE MOVIES?

I DON'T THINK SO.

I hardly ever go! ☺

Kermit, what are the **COWS** here for?

WELL, THEY'RE HERE FOR RAY
AND DALE'S CLOSING NUMBER

What are they singing?

"Catch a Falling *Steer*"?
OR

"If *Heifer* Should
I Leave You"?
WHAT ABOUT

"Moooooooo River"? ☺

HEY GUYS! LOOK AT THESE OLD PHOTOS I FOUND.

CAN YOU BELIEVE THAT **'80S HAIRCUT** I USED TO HAVE?

I LOOKED TOTALLY RIDICULOUS! ☺

TEN OR ELEVEN MILES AWAY! ☺

YEAH, THAT'S THE
ROAD MANAGER.

HE'S THE MAN WITH
THE CONTACTS?

No, he's the man with the van. ☺

HAVE YOU HEARD
THE ONE ABOUT THIS
VERY **FAT** PIG?

HAVE YOU HEARD
THE ONE ABOUT THIS
VERY **FLAT** BEAR?

HIII-
YAH! ☺

A tap-dancing chicken act?

GONZO, I'VE NEVER HEARD OF ANYTHING AS RIDICULOUS AS A DANCING CHICKEN.

HOW
ABOUT A

**TALKING
FROG?** ☺

I FIND THAT MOST PEOPLE DON'T BELIEVE WHAT OTHER PEOPLE TELL THEM.

I don't think that's true. ☺

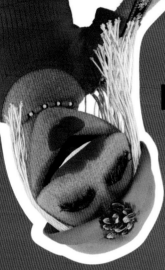

Will you love me forever?

I DON'T KNOW, BABY, ASK ME AGAIN IN A MILLION YEARS. ☺

KERMIT, PLEASE
LET ME BE IN

Pigs in Space!

YOU CAN'T.

WHY CAN'T I BE IN
Pigs in Space?

BECAUSE YOU'RE
NOT A
PIG!

Nobody's perfect. ☺

HMMM. OH, YEAH!

ON YOUR WAY OUT, WOULD YOU EMPTY THE GARBAGE? ☺

I FINALLY FOUND THE
SURE WAY TO LOSE WEIGHT:

I bought a scale that lies! ☺

I WENT TO THE DIET DOCTOR
AND IN JUST TWO MONTHS
I LOST £300! ☺

Oh, my heart!

It's going pitter, patter
... pitter, patter.

YEAH, WELL,
MAYBE YOU'VE HAD
TOO MUCH
COFFEE. ☺

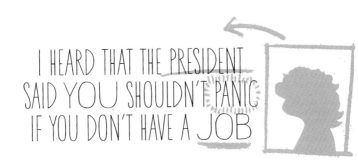

I HEARD THAT THE PRESIDENT SAID YOU SHOULDN'T PANIC IF YOU DON'T HAVE A JOB

That's easy for him to say-
HE'S GOT A JOB!

I HEAR YOU COME FROM A BROKEN HOME.

TWO AMOEBAS WALKED OUT OF A BAR.

ONE AMOEBA SAYS TO THE OTHER,

"Say, is that the sun or the moon?"

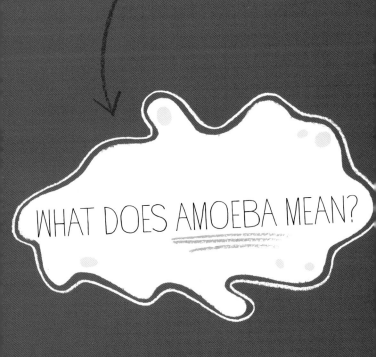

WHAT DOES AMOEBA MEAN?

I don't know.
I don't live around here,
EITHER! ☺

TONIGHT I'M GOING TO PUT SOMETHING NEW IN MY ACT!

I WAS GOING TO GIVE BEAKER
THE HONOUR OF DEMONSTRATING
THIS NEW DIESEL SHAVER.

That's a close shave
for Beaker either way. ☺

Kissy-kissy?

UH, MISS PIGGY
WHILE I AM FLATTERED AT
THIS DISPLAY OF AFFECTION
ALLOW ME TO REMIND YOU
ONCE AGAIN THAT...

I do not want you

Oh, good, then can I have her?

(Cont.)

HIIII-
YAH!

THAT IS KNOWN AS GETTING

TWO TURKEYS

WITH

ONE CHOP. ☺

HERE'S YOUR NEXT PATIENT, DR BOB, HE'S A CONDUCTOR

Well, he's not getting any symphony from **me!**

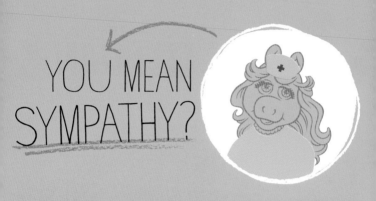

YOU MEAN
SYMPATHY?

He's not getting
any of that, either!☺

WE HAVE MUSIC, COMEDY AND
225 DANCING **ELEPHANTS...**

WHO LEFT THEIR COSTUMES AT HOME
BECAUSE UNFORTUNATELY THEY FORGOT
TO PACK THEIR **TRUNKS.**

113

THEY SAY THE CHILDREN
OF TODAY ARE THE
PARENTS OF TOMORROW.

I thought it took LONGER than that... ☺

WHAT DO YOU DO WHEN SOMEONE GIVES YOU

A LARGE BOULDER AS A PRESENT?

TAKE IT FOR GRANITE! ☺

WOCKA! WOCKA!

HA HA HA HA HA HA HA HA HA HA HA

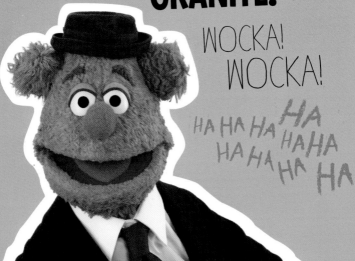

I ONCE MET A
VAMPIRE SO RICH,

**he lived in a
split-level coffin!** ☺

Kermit, what's with all those showgirls?

WE JUST KIND OF THREW THEM IN.

Well, THROW THEM OUT! ☺

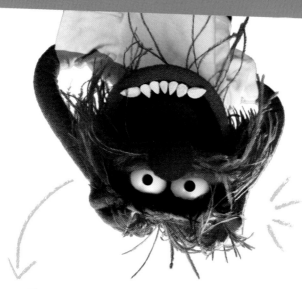

AAAH. You know, I'm falling for you.

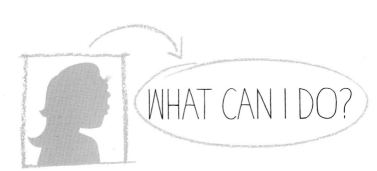

WHAT CAN I DO?

Get out of the WAY!

AAAAH! ☺

IF YOU DON'T MIND,
I'LL DO THE JOKES.

We don't mind, but **WHEN ARE YOU GOING TO DO THEM?** ☺

Index

PAGE

THAT'S ALL FOLKS!

HOPE TO SEE YOU AGAIN AT THE NEXT SHOW!

[HOLD FOR APPLAUSE...]